ASPEN

ASPEN
BLAZON OF THE HIGH COUNTRY

Text by Ann Zwinger
Photographs by Barbara Sparks

GIBBS·SMITH
P
PUBLISHER

PEREGRINE SMITH BOOKS
SALT LAKE CITY

First edition
94 93 92 91   6 5 4 3 2 1

This is a Peregrine Smith Book, published by
Gibbs Smith, Publisher
P.O. Box 667
Layton, Utah 84041

Design by J. Scott Knudsen, Park City, Utah

Manufactured by Dai Nippon, Hong Kong

Cover photographs © 1991 by Barbara Sparks
Inset: *La Veta Pass, Colorado*

Library of Congress Cataloging-in-Publication Data

Zwinger, Ann.
Aspen : blazon of the high country /
text by Ann Zwinger :
photographs by Barbara Sparks.
p. cm.
ISBN 0-87905-324-0
1. Aspen — West (U.S.)
2. Aspen — West (U.S.) — Seasonal variations.
I. Sparks, Barbara. II. Title.
QK495.S16Z95   1991
583'.981—dc20   90-23557
CIP

For Sally Ann Roberts

For Ken, Doug, Ben, Andrea, and Clayton Sparks

PHOTOGRAPHER'S NOTES

For several years I have hiked in the Rocky Mountains with friends. Occasionally we scale a "fourteener"—a mountain that exceeds fourteen thousand feet. The heights and panoramas are breathtaking, but often it is the walk through the aspen forest that has been the elixir of the day.

As a photographer I am drawn to aspen. Autumn's crescendo of aspen gold gilding our mountains is one of nature's spectacular shows. This extravaganza aside, I am stunned by the simplicity of aspen's slim and pristine boles, the infinite variety of branching patterns, the lush understories of summer, the translucent quality of fall leaves, the brindled bark, and above all, the wondrous high-country habitat.

Ann's idea of an aspen book as a parallel study was fascinating. What are the disparate emotions of a naturalist and a photographer? There were many times when our reactions interfaced, but often Ann was absorbed by one spectrum and I another.

Photography is light. Nuances of light . . . always changing. Never quite the same. I gravitate to aspen groves that cast a spell of form, shade, and strong emotions. The impact of weather, first and last light of day, and the whimsey of cloud cover all play a role in selection, while harsh light is the enemy of the photographer. So tied into the caprice of the elements, the photographer is not the best of companions.

We journeyed to northern climes of this country to find thickets of aspen hauntingly oriental in appearance, especially on the east side of Glacier National Park. On the Niwot Ridge in Colorado, at 12,500 feet, I found twisted aspen so stunted by the elements that mature aspen were less than a foot in height. Nature had wrought its own bonsai. On

Kebler Pass and on the Wasatch Plateau we found aspen over a hundred feet in height. Giant aspen on Boulder Mountain in Utah made a miniature of Ann standing beside them. Then there were the uncanny locations of aspen on top of mountains surrounded by a sea of desert below. Such was the experience in the Chiricahua Mountains high above the Chihuahuan Desert in southern Arizona. In the Sierras of California I encountered glorious aspen meadows. I was intrigued in the Toiyabe National Forest in Nevada by older aspen groves that bore the miscellaneous inscriptions of Basque sheepherders who had camped there over a half-century earlier. In Oregon and Washington we found aspen on valley floors as low as two thousand feet. And then full circle, we would return to Colorado and find aspen at fifty-five hundred feet and above—in the high country.

What makes me stop the car, halt my footsteps, or cease my skiing to photograph? It is an accumulation of knowledge that seems to rush together in an instant—an awareness of the moment. It is pure emotion. It is a passion.

There was a certain serendipity in our aspen search in finding special locations no one had mentioned, such as a mottled aspen grove in perfect light that half an hour later might well appear drab and spent. Timing is everything.

The photographs in this book have been taken with predominantly Kodachrome 64 film and occasionally Fujichrome 50. My Olympus OM-1 has interchangeable fixed lenses. My favorite are the 24mm, the 50mm, and the 100mm and the 50mm macro. I photograph with a sky 1-A filter and other filters I use sparingly. Two of the filters I sometimes use are the split density filter and the enhancing filter. All the photographs were taken with available light.

This aspen quest has taken me far beyond my beloved Colorado and New Mexico. No wonder. Aspen are North America's most widely distributed tree and over much of the western part of this country, aspen have a special significance in seasonal drama.

The aspen presented here are as I found them in a certain light in a given season. Another hour, another day, another time of year and the selection would be different. The pursuit is open-ended. Now there are "stashes" of aspen to which I shall always wish to return . . . for other light and other vagaries.

ACKNOWLEDGMENTS

There are many who have helped us in this aspen odyssey. Most important are those scholars who have carried out aspen research over the years, and it is their work that ballasts this book. With appreciation for their scholarship and generosity, we acknowledge them first: Richard Reynolds and Wayne Shepperd, U.S. Forest Service; Alex Vargo and Barbara Winternitz, Colorado College.

In Arizona we thank Bill Broyles for good directions.

In California, Gay Eitel, Lake Tahoe Basin Management Unit, USDA Forest Service; and aspen aficionados Shirley and Michael Klynn at Fallen Leaf Lake.

In Colorado, Jack Armit for getting us from here to there; Audrey Benedict, White Cloud Naturalists; Kathy Brazelton, National Park Service; Alfred Hagedorn, rancher; Dick and Judy Noyes, Chinook Bookshop; William Preston and Tim Cooper, Gordon's Books; Joyce Gellhorn, biologist, Boulder; Lee Sayre, Paonia; Sandy Sanborn, Sanborn Western Camps.

In Idaho, Mary Dugan, Twin Falls Ranger District; Ginger Plotter, Ketchum Community Library, Regional History Library; Cort Conley, author and boatman extraordinaire, Cambridge; Art Selin, (Twin Falls) Sawtooth National Forest; Ken and Heather Britton, Sawtooth National Forest, for letting us photograph inscribed aspen in their yard; Jim Myers, Silviculturist, Idaho Panhandle National Forest; Mary Wagoner, Twin Falls Forester, Sawtooth National Forest.

In Montana, Beth Dunagen, Information Specialist, Glacier National Park; Carl Fielder, School of Forestry, University of Montana; Maxine and Buzz Johnson, Bigfork; Jim VanDenburg, Flathead National Forest.

In Nevada, Virgil Anderson, fire ranger, Toiyabe National Forest.

In New Mexico, Michael Chavez, Los Cordovas woodworker and former high-country sheepherder.

In Oregon, Bob Losanto, Butte Falls rancher; Fred McDonald, natural resource specialist, BLM, Burns; Bill Hopkins, Area Ecologist at Bend, Deschutes National Forest Supervisor; Dick Dezellem, Winema National Forest; and Mr. and Mrs. Kent Roberts, Portland, for the loan of a four-wheel-drive car when we needed it most.

In Utah, Don Moser, Escalante Ranger District; Don T. Nebeker, Uinta National Forest; Jerry Griffin, Uinta National Forest; Ken Sleight, Pack Creek Ranch; Suthey Swede, Capitol Reef Inn, Torrey; Oma Wilcox for much-appreciated hospitality, Layton; Terry Tempest Williams, naturalist, Salt Lake City.

In Washington, Marti Ames, Public Affairs Specialist, Wenatchee National Forest; Cris Gibbs, Secretary, and Bob Stoehr, Silviculturist, Leavenworth District, Wenatchee National Forest.

In Wyoming, Dr. Alan Beetle, Professor Emeritus, University of Wyoming; Roy A. Renkin, Biological Technician, and Ed Varley, Chief Research Biologist, Yellowstone National Park.

Our deepest appreciation to Madge Baird for clear-eyed, precise editing, and to Scott Knudsen for the elegant book design: both took our vision of this book and fashioned it into the eloquent statement we wished it to be; and to Gibbs Smith for great encouragement and guidance.

Each of us is indebted to others for specific help and we thank them individually. Barbara thanks Jo and David Hill, Cliff Reynolds, Carol and Mack Trapp, Barbara and Frank Waters, Kathy Beamer, Vince Fazzi, and her persevering and loving family. Ann thanks Kate Belden, Ruby Frice, Timilou Rixon, Sara and Kent Roberts, and particularly Wayne Shepperd, U.S. Forest Service, for such a careful reading of the manuscript that any errors remaining are woefully hers.

ASPEN

Aspen first captivated me by their visual splendor: the resonance of their autumns, the eloquence of their springs, the opulence of their summers, the elegance of their winters. Then an aspen grove at eighty-three hundred feet in the Colorado Rockies, at a place our family named Constant Friendship after an ancestor's farm in Virginia, became a permanent part of my life; and the enchantment with the rhythms of bole and background, of sound and silence, of change and survival still times my comings and goings, measures my year.

The aspen odyssey for this book drew Barbara and me north to the Canadian and south to the Mexican borders, to the mountains of Arizona, where aspen grow on cooler north-facing slopes, and to the hills of Montana, where they grow on warmer south-facing slopes. Aspen normally occur as a relatively continuous band of montane trees below spruce-fir forests, and so we have seen them in Arizona, California, Nevada, New Mexico, and Wyoming; in more scattered patches they grace the hillsides of Idaho, Oregon, and Washington. Most of all, we enjoyed the munificence of four million acres of aspen glorifying Colorado and Utah.

Through all these trips the aspen grove at Constant Friendship remains the baseline against which I understand other groves. It is here that I first saw a weasel in winter pelage and found a vole busying through its grassy tunnel, first listened to a yellow-bellied sapsucker drill its endless holes, first learned about bark beetles and gormandizing beavers. Here I swished a butterfly net after a Wiedermeyer's admiral, slept among the aspen daisies on a midsummer night's eve, found spring's first violets, sketched the black-eyed Susans and wild roses, mourned a fall and dreamed away a winter, was attacked by the winds of my own incertitudes, light-pruned my own branches, and calibrated the seasons of my heart.

 # WINTER

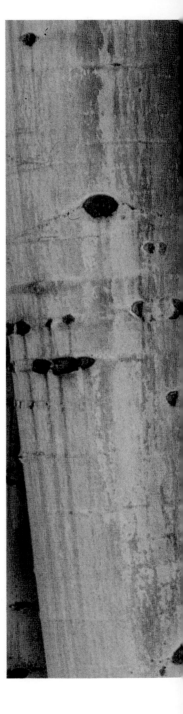

Half-past January, the aspen grove at Constant Friendship reverses to a negative: white feathered branches web a dark gray sky. Supercooled fog floated in last night and, when it touched the aspen branches, spiked them with fine, granular rime ice. The frosting holds thicker on the webbing of branches at the top of the canopy, a white tent now luffing in the morning breeze. Despite the uncommonness of the special conditions that create this accumulation of ice, it can add a precious inch of water a year.

The mists shred, baring ragged blue scraps of sky. As ice in the canopy melts, the falling drops fracture the light like blazing prisms, and the grove shimmers with an ethereal opalescence. By noon the magic is gone, leaving ordinary trees against an ordinary sky.

One cloudy winter Sunday morning on Steens Mountain in Oregon, the aspen boles look vertically striped, sunlit on one side, shadowed on the other, despite the fact there's no sun. The "shadows" are in truth a sharp shift in bole color. Nose-close, hieroglyphics of dove and oyster and pearl white and the palest gray-green intermingle across the bark. The whiter side of the trunk faces toward the outer edge of the grove while the inner side is darker, tinged with the decided green of chlorophyll, the joining of the delicate colors netted together by a lacy tracery. I scratch the bark with my fingernail and find a white protective outer layer of tissue, the periderm, overlying the green.

On most trees, outer bark is formed of layers of dead cork cells. As new growth expands on inner layers, the surface layers of dead cells split and break into the furrowed patterns such as those on pine or elm. In

Gore Wilderness, Colorado

aspen, periderm cells continually grow, divide, and expand with the tree's increasing diameter. Throughout the life of the tree, the protective periderm maintains the same relative thickness by adding new cells from beneath as it sluffs off the outer cells as a chalky powder. The smooth, thin periderm is delicate and easily breached, making aspen one of the most susceptible of trees to a wide variety of injuries: fire and lightning, animals and insects, and many pathogens.

Aspen are unique among northern trees in having photosynthetic bark (to the south, trees with green bark, like palo verde, are common). The ability of aspen to photosynthesize almost year-round, even at temperatures below freezing, adds about 2 percent to the tree's net photosynthesis. Meager as it is, that addition is enough to aid stressed trees in their recovery after insect damage or unseasonal frosts, and to permit aspen to grow in a predominantly coniferous ecosystem.

In winter, trees on the exposed outer edge of the grove are especially susceptible to sunscald. The whitened periderm protects the boles from this kind of heat damage. On bright winter days, high altitude sun blasts the sunny side of the tree; yet, if temperatures are low enough (as they often are in the mountains), the bark will freeze when clouds block the sun; when the sun comes out, the growing layer of cambium beneath the periderm may thaw within minutes. This alternate freezing and thawing causes cell breakage that results in scar tissue. Whiter-barked trees have higher reflectance values and are less vulnerable. Although sunscald itself is seldom fatal, it renders the tree vulnerable to the many diseases that aspen is heir to.

Alas, the smooth, pale bark is irresistible to immortality-seekers who would carve JOHN LOVES MARY. Such cutting opens the bark to all kinds of infections, and the future is bleak for aspen growing around campsites.

In southern Utah, the crescent moon has long since set over the plateau, absorbed into the western horizon. As the sky lightens, aspen boles glow ghostly, dressed in shrouds. Smaller aspen ring the taller trees of the inner grove; the dense growth of the stand allows little reproduction within its shade, and so new growth springs up at the edge and circles the clone like a petticoat ruffle.

Clone derives from the Greek word for *twig* or *slip*, which infers propagation by hand, and indeed many nursery plants are cloned for a reliable sameness of plants. A clone is an aggregate of individual organisms descended by asexual reproduction from a single individual (originally produced sexually), rendering all members of the clone genetically identical.

In the early light the twigging patterns between clones are sharp and distinct. In one clone twigs grow in repetitive short curves, Arabian calligraphy scribed on a parchment sky; another's twigs are as straight as if soldered on, a sculpture in silver. A third clone contains **Y** trees that branch about twenty feet from the base to create a double crown—unusual, as aspen tend to grow as single stems. Another clone contains very tall and slender trees with minimal frizzled crowns, as if the trunks had frayed out like a piece of yarn, giving this clone a stalky, gawky quality.

Aspen grow in clones because of their preferred method of reproduction: they send out sprouts or suckers, called ramets, from established ropelike lateral roots that snake within six inches of the soil surface; new members of the clone will have, among many other similarities, the same sex, since aspen is dioecious (either male or female), the same bark color and branching habit, and will break dormancy at the same time.

Leafing time between clones can vary up to a month, depending upon each clone's reaction to temperature. I recall a gentle six-hundred-foot slope stalked with aspen clones, above a branch of Cut Bank Creek in Montana. The unleafed crowns appeared hazed with mauve. The adjacent clone had just flushed, spreading breathless green across the canopy. Sun spotlighted the next a vivid green. On a fourth, the pale trunks of still-winter, unleafed trees crosshatched the slope. Later at Mt. Timpanogos in Utah, we saw the sequence autumn-reversed, with some clones gilt, some still verdant, and some salmon-red (a combination of a slow-cooling autumn and a genetic-based disposition toward scarlet), and some bare-boned as each clone dropped its leaves in its own time.

Each clone has its own predisposition to insect attack, to frost damage, to the aging cycle, and to disease resistance and suscepibility. Big black splotches created a startling black-and-white effect throughout a clone in Idaho. The big, rough, gnarled excrescences of cankers, bulging and swelling, broke out on every bole. The whole clone was diseased. Its neighbor was clean.

In contrast to these varied mid-altitude clones, aspen growing at their upper limit tend to look alike. In Colorado at 12,500 feet, they are part of the krummholtz—dwarfed trees fashioned by wind and ice. Farther north, on Altyn Peak in Montana, they grow only two-and-a-half to three feet high at half that altitude. The severity of the environment molds them all to the shape of survival.

The sun is briefly warm this February afternoon as I idle through the grove at Constant Friendship, stopping by a small tree with an open oval of bared wood six inches wide and two feet long. Surrounding the scar is a canker, a plump swelling of bark that looks like a horse's collar, scribed with fine concentric lines that mark each year of the canker's growth. Shiny reddish-brown varnish drizzles down the trunk, the tree's reaction to boring-beetle holes through which the infection likely entered.

In spring when the growing part of the tree, the cambium, is producing new tissue, the tree forms a canker—callus tissue that isolates the infection. When the fungus invaded the new cambium during the winter dormant season, it forced the tree to form more scar tissue the following spring, resulting in successive growth lines. Since this fungus grows more quickly vertically than it does horizontally, it may take up to eighty years for it to encompass and girdle the bark on this tree, finally cutting off the flow of water, killing the tree.

Trees that don't even reach my waist are already knobby with galls and calluses, like street urchins, bitten with knowledge beyond their years. In winter's bleak light, the bare aspen reveal all the rigors of survival that are hidden by the dancing shadows of summer foliage. Leafless, the miseries truly show—all the cankers and blisters, the arthritis and the broken bones.

And yet, I have never seen the grove more beautiful, the boles pearl gray figured with charcoal, the quintessence of formal elegance.

Gloved and booted and capped, defiant of March, I wander the aspen grove only to find that winter has gone elsewhere, leaving behind the chill debris of its tantrums. Wind still sizzles through the tops of the aspen, making them chirp like crickets. Spring may be dawdling, there will be more snows and nights of clanging cold, but winter, bored with it all, has left.

The wind struts in from somewhere west and sways the upper half of the trees, sashays on through, taking its sound with it. It works the boles individually: one ticks like a metronome, another scribes circles on the sky, another draws ellipses, each translating the wind in its own way.

It's been an efficient wind this winter. Not a single leaf still hangs above but thousands layer the floor beneath, their undersides buff, their uppers bright russet. Black fungus peppers the undersurface of every leaf, clustering along the veins as pin-pricks of soot, aggregating into dots. On the leaf's upper side, the protective waxy layer of cells scales off in gray flakes like dry skin.

I gather a bouquet of leaves, stems still sinewy and strong, flattened at the leaf base, authorities on the physics of fluttering. Hence their scientific name, *Populus tremuloides*, given to them by French botanist André Michaux in 1803. The superstitious *coureurs du bois*, French-Canadian woodsmen of the seventeenth century, gave them their common name of "quakies" because they believed that *le tremble* furnished the wood of the Cross and has quaked ever since.

Once out of the dampness of the litter, the leaves curl and crisp, the torque of drying pulling open the hidden cracks into slots and holes. One leaf puckers at the stem but its edges remain intact, fringed with a breath of white hairs; a second folds its margins into a scoop; others twist where necessary, crimp where needed. Each leaf encompasses in its sandwich of cells the knowledge of how to expand in the warmth of spring, how to process water and chlorophyll into carbohydrates in the heat of summer, how to suffer the loss of water and the chill of autumn, how to release and fall free, and how to dissemble gracefully into the damp earth to become a new beginning. And to all of them clings the distinctive, sweetly cloying odor of aspen.

Against the buttermilk sky the top branches of this particular grove of aspen splay upward in repeated supplicant curves. None have swelling leaf buds yet, except one small tree at the edge of the grove whose upper branches look knotted, so full are they with burgeoning buds. Considering that this aspen grove, like all aspen groves, is a clone of genetically identical individuals that go about the year in synchrony, something is awry.

I find a clothesline tied around the budding tree about ten feet off the ground. Once it lashed a bough between it and a nearby tree, and from that bough hung a swing. In a rush, out of memory comes the scent of summertime and the lilt of children's voices at play. Over the years the cord weathered to the color of the bark and I forgot it, and now the choked trunk bulges over it. Although the tree's crown may be completely severed from its root system, buds expand with catkins this one last year, exhausting the tree's final supply of stored carbohydrates and water.

In this time of implied spring and new growth, this tree is dying, and too early sends out defiant springtime buds with nature's insistence on life.

Giant aspen south of Crater Lake National Park, Oregon

Isolated aspen grove, typical of Sawtooth Valley, Idaho

Aspen growing in drainage, Steens Mountain, Oregon

Aspen "eye" branch scar, result of self-pruning

San Juan Mountains, Colorado

Sawtooth National Forest, Idaho

Rime on aspen, Wenatchee National Forest, Washington

Aspen canker

Winter storm, White River National Forest, Colorado

Aspen clone with chevron branching pattern, near Mt. McLaughlin, Oregon

Lizard Head Pass, San Juan Mountains, Colorado

S P R I N G

On this day-before-spring morning the ground at Constant Friendship turns to muck, and pocket-gopher "eskers"—the dirt trails left from burrowing at the interface between snow and soil—snake out from the last patches of snow. During the winter the pocket gopher, the most prevalent mammal in aspen groves almost everywhere, worked the grove from beneath the snow cover, scarfing up roots and rhizomes. Soils within the grove seldom freeze deeply enough under the snowpack to hinder a pocket gopher's meanderings, even though soils in clearings outside may be hard frozen.

Now that the ground is thawing, the pocket gopher, who feeds only a few hours a day, begins its retreat underground. There it contributes to the richness of the soil by turning over a ton or more of soil per acre, increasing soil porosity, adding organic matter, nitrogen, and phosphate.

Pocket-gopher mounds wind through clones in Montana, dry out in Utah, leave dirt squiggles in Nevada and New Mexico—sinuous pathways marking a cloistered, solitary existence and the virtues of an underground vegetarian diet.

Near the Canadian border of Montana, aspen patch the distant hillsides in a mosaic of clones, greige with tinges of olive or rose or apricot, hues muted to ghosts of colors, approaching the time of leaf flush. Along the road, aspen patches nestle between moraines—hillocks formed when glaciers paused in their retreat and dumped their load of debris. Isolated clones grow no higher than the top of the moraine, pruned back by icy winds to a tangle of branches in which the sky lays clouds. These patchy lower-altitude groves correspond closely to the ground moraines of the

Pasque flower, kinnikinnik, and aspen

last glaciation of the Ice Age. Growing on glaciated soil, these younger clones more closely resemble the aspen of New England than the larger, older aspen of Utah and Colorado.

On this beautifully bleak day as I stand standing on rough rocky soil that glistens with moisture, I visualize a pear-shaped, sesame-sized seed finding a damp, protected microsite one suitable summer millennia ago. Fossil aspen leaves from fifteen million years ago, found in paleo-environments much like the wetter parts of their present-day range, are widespread in the West. Two species of aspen, with slightly different habitat requirements, grew close enough some fifty thousand years ago that they could have hybridized to give rise to the single species of modern aspen. Scientists conjecture that the specific climatic conditions conducive to seedling establishment of modern clones may have been met during a wetter, cooler time, such as the close of the last Ice Age ten thousand years ago.

Aspen seeds sprout quickly, germinating in a few hours within a wide temperature range from freezing to nearly a hundred degrees, able to send up a sprout in three days. But continuing survival is rare. Being so tiny, the seed contains minimum nutrition to tide over the seedling, and the delicate new sprout relies solely on a minute cluster of root hairs for water and nutrients. It cannot survive without generous and continuing moisture, and in the West soils commonly dry out before a root system can develop. Chance litter snuffs out its light, and high heat is as detrimental as freezing. That is not to say that aspen do not grow from seed today in the West, but that is the exception rather than the rule.

All in all, for aspen in the western United States, reproducing by seed is a very chancy affair and vegetative reproduction an advantageous one. A ramet that sprouts from a rootstock draws nourishment from an already established root system and requires less moisture than a seedling. It can flower earlier, giving its seeds a competitive edge over other later-flowering trees, undoubtedly playing a role in aspen's wide distribution.

A single seedling, sprouted and successfully growing, can begin a new clone, and foresters find scattered seedlings today in clearcuts and elsewhere. Still, aspen reproduce primarily by vegetative means, reducing the opportunity for new genetic combinations, limiting aspen's ability to adapt to changing environments. But aspen's penchant for vegetative reproduction, rather than the individuality and variation available through sexual reproduction, allows aspen to flourish as the most widespread deciduous tree in North America.

In May we crest the Continental Divide in Montana at Marias Pass. At 5,060 feet the aspen are as bare as those we just left in Colorado, even though we are more than 3,000 feet lower. Small and stunted, trunks wavy and quirked, they grow in little copses, wind-bent toward the east. One thicket of trees scarcely eight feet tall is wind-pruned into as many curves as a helix. All the trees are "pistol-butted" at the base, having suffered burdens of heavy snow when they were young. In northern Montana where aspen grow at their upper altitudinal limit, there is little regeneration and seeds have low viability. Growing in such small clones, they lose the protection afforded by a large group of trees and become more subject to damage by winter's desiccating squalls.

These trees have a persona, an energy, that righteous trees with tall, straight boles lack. In the next clone the gamin trees lean, jammed together like people in a subway car when it brakes, all tilting at a twenty-degree angle. In another clone, positive and negative curves tangle together in endless variety, the trees composed like a modern dance piece—a frieze of figures interwoven for effect. At their feet are hundreds of glacier lilies with pert, upturned petals and sepals, as cheerful as daffodils, blooming at the dank end of spring before summer leaves filter out the sunlight.

One tiny, timorous group of aspen is salmon-tinged from newly dropped catkins composed of many tiny flowers. I pull off a catkin, place it on my topo map and fish out my hand lens. The brown-fringed scales of a female flower fall off easily, exposing a bare, translucent green bell, and the two-lobed, bright red stigmas that give the catkins their rosy cast of color from a distance. Pollinated by wind, the flowers need offer neither bright petals nor complex shapes and nectar to attract insects. Considering that on a healthy tree with many hundred catkins, each catkin may have up to a hundred flowers which can produce up to a hundred capsules with six to eight tufted, wind-carried seeds capable of traveling two hundred miles, the potential reproductive capacity per tree is astronomical.

Under the heat of my hand, infinitesimal mites that were hidden in the flowers pour out of the catkins and drop onto the map, traversing printed contour lines, spanning blue-inked ponds, climbing mountains and crossing rivers with eight-legged seven-league boots.

The aspen at Constant Friendship are just leafing out when I return. As I thread a path through them this late spring morning, something in peripheral vision catches my attention. About five feet off the ground, fresh scrapings of four- to five-inch-long narrow ovals are cut through to fresh tan wood. Remarkable—this is the first time in almost thirty years that I have seen these trees barked by elk. Most of the tooth marks are diagonal, as if the elk positioned its head to get a better sample. There are more than a dozen trees so marked, most with one to a few scrapes, typical since elk seldom girdle a tree unless under severe stress, usually taking only a bite here, a bite there.

Elk bark aspen even when other browse is available, which suggests that aspen may contain some substance needed for physiological reasons; willow twigs contain salicylic acid, one of the ingredients in aspirin, and possibly the related aspen offers something of the same. The bark, being soft, is easily removed, about half digestible, and obviously palatable. These superficial scars will darken into scar tissue, but today they are as obvious as a raw gouge on a freshly enameled tabletop.

Elk and aspen are almost synonymous in the West, and aspen stands on the first day of hunting season are not good places for hikers to be. Although small rodents gnaw it near the ground, elk is the only big game animal to eat aspen bark. Deer and moose, as well as elk, feed on new sprouts. Deer tend to browse trees early in the season while moose utilize them in late summer, stripping the foliage from the ramets. Although the new suckers have a high concentration of unpalatable terpenes and resins, they make highly nutritious forage with good protein and crude fat.

There are other, more destructive, teeth marks on the aspen grove at Constant Friendship. Like elk, the distribution of beaver closely matches that of aspen. Some ten years ago an ancient, grizzled beaver hoisted itself slowly, slowly upon the far shore of the pond late one Saturday afternoon. I fretted that it would not survive the winter.

The next spring a younger beaver moved in, and the following year the kits were born. I delighted in watching them while they dammed the streams and cut a few aspen. They also cut willows, but it was the aspen that enchanted them and that they began to ravish with relish.

After the beavers cleaned out aspen conveniently close to water, they worked outward several hundred yards, cutting most trees in late fall in preparation for winter, to repair their lodges and build stockpiles of food. A beaver needs to cut enough trees to furnish two to four pounds of aspen bark a day and to keep its teeth ground down, since they grow continually. During a year a beaver requires an estimated fifteen hundred pounds of food, which can read out to two hundred trees felled, and of those, a beaver may eat only half of what it cuts, leaving the rest to rot.

Soon the beavers had devastated a horrendous swath of aspen, leaving a score teetering on a splinter and a carnage of unused boles on the ground. Even though vigorous sprouting followed their ravages, mature aspen will not reappear within the beavers' life span nor, I have wryly thought many times, within mine. We fell afoul of each other only because human me could not tolerate losing the aspen grove. After several years of repeated and unsuccessful efforts to have the beavers live-trapped and relocated, I left town when they had to be shot. I have never come to terms with my need to keep and theirs to cut.

As I sit writing I hear the sure sign of spring in an aspen grove: the rapid bursts of a yellow-bellied sapsucker's BR-R-R-RR-RR-UP reverberates through the air, defining his territory and announcing his presence to arriving females.

I echolocate this sapsucker and spot him drilling his nest facing the open edge of the stand. He braces against the bole and, with a triphammer head capable of a hundred blows per second, sprays wood chips at my feet. The tree he attacks has prominent conks shelving out on the trunk, a visual sign of interior rot that the sapsucker easily locates by tapping. The hoof-shaped conks are the hard, fruiting bodies of white heartrot, *Fomes igniarius*, a nearly universal fungus that is the most common cause of aspen mortality. A perennial, the conk forms one row of tubes each year through which billions of spores are discharged into the air. The untold number of spores floating around in the air or forming the normal bark microflora do no damage to a healthy tree, but enter any wound, whether from fire scars, beetle exit or entry holes, knots where branches have fallen, or wanton carvings. The fungus spreads outward from the heartwood until it reaches and kills the growing layer of cambium.

The conk is a visual signal to the sapsucker that he need only break through a thin band of healthy, firm outer wood before reaching the soft, diseased wood beneath. Sapsuckers prefer large trees for nesting, and it is in these that heartrot is most extensive. Sapsuckers also feed on aspen sap, characteristically puncturing a series of holes around the trunk that with age become a Morse code of black spots. The sap contains sugars and primary sucroses in substantial amounts, and sapsuckers seem to recognize that the repeated wounding brings the most sap to the surface.

The aspen grove this morning is atwitter with birds, an orchestration of chirps and whistles, tssps and tee-whees. The presence of cavity-drillers such as sapsuckers and woodpeckers, who provide nest sites for hole-nesters who do not generally excavate their own, accounts for the high density of birds in an aspen grove; up to 50 percent of the breeding birds in an aspen grove may be hole-nesters. To have ready-made housing is a boon for the small insectivorous birds who find ample food there: chickadees, warblers, pygmy and white-breasted nuthatches, warbling vireos, violet green and tree swallows, western peewees, wrens, and flycatchers, as well as an occasional predatory owl or falcon.

Years ago we provided the resident sapsucker with a tin roof, and this morning he forsakes the aspen for ear-shattering drum rolls on the corrugated metal, doubtless an amorous entreaty no sapsucker female within hearing distance can refuse.

Fomes igniarius conk on aspen bole

Elk among spring aspen

Aspen and willows, Pikes Peak region, Colorado

Aspen catkins

Aspen catkins, detail

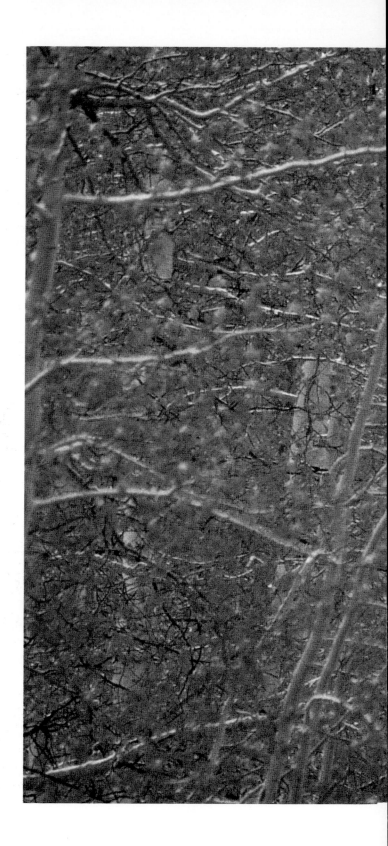

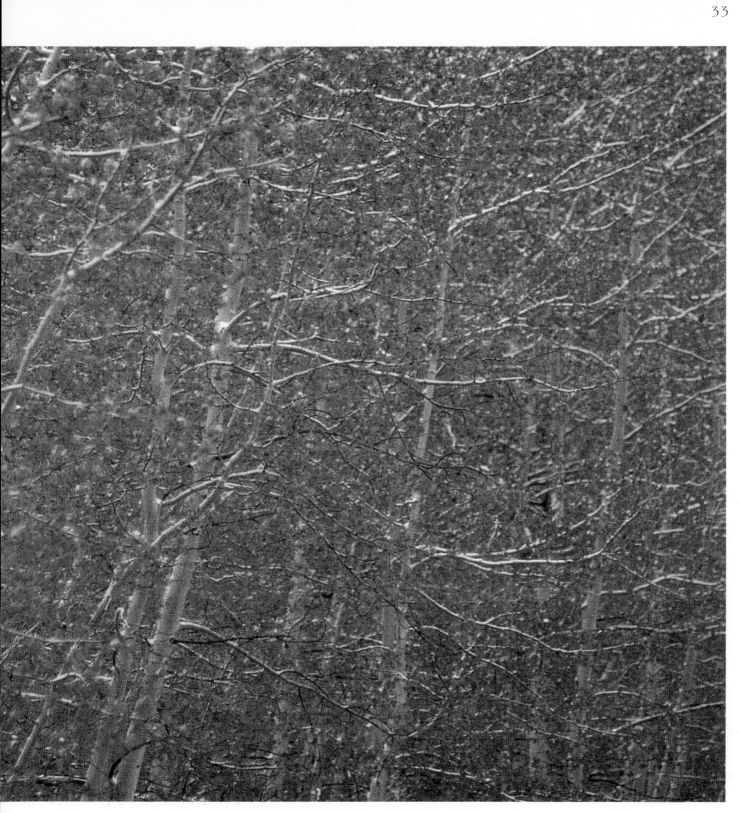

Ute Pass, Colorado

Glacier lilies under snow-warped aspen, Marias Pass, Montana

Aspen thicket, Blackfeet Indian Reservation, Montana

Mosaic of aspen clones above Cut Bank Creek, Montana

Clonal variation in leaf flush, Wolf Creek Pass, Colorado

☘ SUMMER

Willows have leafed, wild strawberries bloom at Constant Friendship. Twenty after eight in the morning, early June, and the first spring azures flirt among the new-leafed branches of the aspen. An eight-foot tree dangles tender half-inch leaflets already riddled and pocked. *Western Forest Insects* lists thirty-four insects that specifically munch, mine, and suck on aspen, and this slender tree looks as if it had been struck by all of them in a picture book illustration of who eats aspen leaves and how.

A young spider mite, a pin-prick of red, rolls across one leaf. It makes the pinkish eighth-inch galls—puffed on top, hollow on the underside— that stud many leaves. Other leaves are gnawed to lace. There is just enough of a green island on one leaf to hold the chewers who skeletonized it: six stubby-bodied, eighth-inch, black larvae of *Chrysomela* leaf beetles, feeding gregariously as they do when very young. Discommoded when I pick the leaf, one crawls up the stem, turns back and jostles in alongside the others, flipping its tail up and down like a beaver slapping water. When disturbed, this larva can also emit a drop of evil-smelling fluid that discourages predators; danger over, the larva retracts the droplet, preserving it for another defense. When full grown, the larva will pupate by hanging head down from the underside of an aspen leaf and emerge as a small, compact, tan beetle with black spots.

An inchworm, a caterpillar of a ubiquitous geometrid moth, aspen-leaf green and a quarter-inch long, slowly loops its way along a leaf margin. The larvae of Wiedermeyer's admiral, a lovely black-and-white butterfly, also prefer aspen. These butterflies are confined to the aspen-willow zone in a narrow strip along the eastern slope of the Rocky Mountains from Colorado to mid-New Mexico. I remember one perching

Lupine, ragwort, and Indian paintbrush beneath aspen, El Dorado National Forest, California

at the end of a sunny branch and lifting off in characteristic floating flight, as insouciant as a summer's day.

Several thin black lines slightly pucker one leaf. One of the lines turns out not to be blackened tissue but an inch-long caterpillar sporting twenty-four yellow spots, two anal tubes on its turned-up tail, and 'ears' on its head. This dashing creature is the summer child of a non-tent-making tent caterpillar moth that hovers about our lights on summer evenings. *Malacosoma disstria* is a smallish moth, light brown, gently barred on inch-span wings attached to a broad, furry body. The smaller male moths are easily distinguished from females by their feathery antennae; they live but a week without feeding, fertilizing eggs that will be laid in August. Exploding populations and heavy infestations defoliate and weaken aspen; if they don't kill the trees, such moth attacks are usually followed by fungus infections or, at best, remove enough photosynthesizing tissue to upset growth regulation processes.

In turn, the caterpillars are attacked by two species of ants who trundle them off to their nests near the base of the aspen. Worker ants constantly prowl aspen trunks and branches to forage or tend their aphid colonies, most species of which secrete a honeydew that ants avidly seek. There are aphids aplenty this morning, pale green minutiae crowding on the backs of leaves or encrusting stems, puncturing plant tissue with their beaks, often infecting aspen with fungus or other pathogens.

Minute leafhopper larvae occupy other leaves, visible as shadows when sunlight shines through the young, translucent tissue. A tiny wedge-headed adult, already laying eggs, cuts a slit into a new twig, one more wound for the little tree. I plop down beneath this tree to take notes, and little green leafhoppers suddenly rain on my notebook page, popping on the paper like drops of water on a hot skillet.

Aspen garland Jenny Lake at the foot of the magnificent Grand Tetons. Leafblotch miners wind elegant serpentine paths through succulent green cells, feeding between the upper and lower cuticle. These miners are the tiny, very flat larvae of small, colorful moths with fringed wings, each species of which makes its own characteristic mine.

In a clone backed up a hillside several miles east, the aspen boles look unblemished, smoothly bandaged, with branch scars uncannily eyelike, complete with upper and lower lid, white centered with a black iris and pupil. But the understory of the clone contains multitudes of young aspen, their leaves riddled by aspen-leaf miners.

Young aspen are extremely susceptible to fungus attack and new shoots fronting this clone are already beleaguered. At the ends of several small branches, the blackened branch tips are as hooked as a "shepherd's crook," the common name of *Pollaccia radiosa*, the fungus that attacks new terminal shoots.

Some of the young stems have put out second-growth leaves, large and un-aspen looking. These, too, are gnawed and pierced, and aphids crowd the tender stems. When leaf damage is heavy, a second leafing of abnormally sized and shaped leaves can appear within three weeks. This rapid response to defoliation may help the tree survive almost incessant insect attacks. Early leaves are pre-formed in winter buds and are all typical aspen size and shape; secondary shoots spring from lateral buds. Not only are secondary leaves aberrant with gland-tipped teeth, but the characteristic flattened petiole is round so that these leaves cannot flutter as aspen leaves should. These odd-looking shoots are a glimpse of what aspen would be like if they weren't aspen.

On a shoulder of Utah's Mt. Nebo, bright lavender thistles front a row of spindly aspen. I can easily encircle any stem with my fingers, garnering a chalky powder on my hands. The leaves that still hang from these trees are an odd light green, and they fall thus, without yellowing first. Every leaf is chocolate-spattered with fungus, blemishes of the common leaf blight *Marssonnina populi*. The spores drop with the season's twig and leaf fall, persist over winter, and infect new trees during late- spring wet periods. Not a lot is known about the extent of its damage other than trees infested with leaf blight produce small leaves, and early leaf drop often defoliates trees in the summer. The dismal aspect of this grove is countered by a vigorous wreath of new suckers and lusty regeneration.

In July we come to Yellowstone after the massive fires, not knowing what to expect, steeled to see a park reported as "in ashes." Instead we find lupine and fireweed lavished across a hillside of burned aspen, sweeps of brilliant green grass and thousands of acres of untouched trees. Wildflowers grow so thickly in the swales I can't see my feet. Swallows swing through the air, butterflies loop over a Botticelli carpet of blossoms, penstemons intermix with lupine, yarrow, cinquefoil, yellow hawksbeard and thistles, fireweed, wild geranium, and the yellow seedpods beyond number of pennycress.

Nevertheless, fire signs are conspicuous. In a small but intense burn area, one fifteen-inch diameter aspen is blackened only on its lower half, while its upper retains normal color. Aspen bark is not fire resistant and aspen are easily killed by fire. Fires usually burn only the outer trees of the clone, but fire intensity often varies widely, from fires which don't disrupt the aspen leaf canopy, to intense fires that leave a charred pyre of aspen boles. The Park Service estimates that about one-third of the aspen in Yellowstone were affected by the fire.

At noon we explore a burn where about a quarter of the clone lies on the ground. A tremendous firestorm blasted the aspen here, bent the tops of still-standing trees, but felled most of them that now lie all pointing the same direction, a carnage of ebony trunks. Blackened soil crunches underfoot. The burn areas release a distinctive odor—not the unpleasant, acrid, doused-campfire smell I expect, but a clearer odor of sunlight on charcoal and dark heat rising. Big pink granite boulders lie half-buried, heat-cracked and disintegrating, their exposed faces flaking off like big cornflakes, already breaking down to become soil. Apricot-colored day-flying moths cloud up out of sky-blue lupine patches, a frivolous, flighty dance of colors against the funereal black of the burnt aspen.

Closeby I tally fifty-three new aspen shoots within a ten-foot radius of a gutted tree. Most are a foot high, all have large, healthy, clean leaves. Such luxurious sprouting seldom occurs under ordinary circumstances because of a process called apical dominance. Auxin, a growth-regulating hormone, is continually produced at the apex of the tree and cycled to the roots, where it inhibits new growth. When fire destroys the crown, auxin production stops, auxin levels in the roots drop, and new shoots can proliferate. In their turn, the rapidly growing ramets produce auxins that circulate to the roots to prevent the development of additional suckers which could overload the roots' capacity to nourish. Growth of these initial shoots is fast the first year, less the second as more energy goes to producing lateral branches. Most of these ramets will become independent of their parent root system at the end of this first growing season, although some may remain connected as long as a quarter of a century.

Aspen in Yellowstone have declined by an estimated 50 percent in less than a hundred years, accompanied by a marked increase in fire-sensitive species like big sagebrush and conifers, especially in the northern park, where twenty- to twenty-five-year fire cycles were more frequent in the past. Present clones are mostly in the 100–150-year overmature range, increasingly subject to disease, lacking new growth, and invaded by conifers which will eventually shade them out. The usual widespread proliferation of aspen after fires may not occur this time, due to a combination of depleted root stocks, heavy elk browsing, climatic conditions, and a change in groundwater availability.

Aspen need several years to grow to the six or eight feet that puts them out of the browsing range of elk, and for years the decline in the aspen at Yellowstone was thought to be too many elk eating too many young aspen. Many biologists believe that current fire suppression policies on federal lands is a greater determinant, along with a change to a climate less hospitable to aspen: aspen thrive on sixteen to forty inches plus of rain, cold winters and cool summers; they do not tolerate long periods of high temperature or the dryness of the current climate.

Aspen depend upon wildfire for healthy reproduction and rejuvenation of overmature groves. Fire cycles were always a part of the Wyoming ecosystem until 1866 when the U.S. Cavalay was assigned to fight fires and protect the park. In the twentieth century "Smokey the Bear" ads fostered the idea that all fires are bad. Biologists note the other side of the equation: after-fire rejuvenation of forests, creation of more wildlife habitat, and increased productivity. After a fire the herbaceous understory burgeons with newly released soil nutrients with an increased diversity of species. A burn releases carbon to the air and large amounts of nitrogen into the soil, and at the same time kills the insects and fungi that are the bane of aspen.

Some ecosystems not only are adapted to but depend upon fire for their well-being. In the palm oases of the Mojave Desert, fire kills the palm bark borer and rejuvenates the groves; fire maintains the tall-grass prairies of the Midwest. Aspen is an admirably adapted, fire-dependent species. In the East it is bacteria and fungi that break down dead organic matter and recycle the nutrients contained in it that would otherwise be locked up and unavailable for new growth. In the West, it is fire.

Whether or not aspen are disappearing in the Yellowstone area may also hinge on the definition of a "successful" aspen as a tree. On a dry bench above the Lamar River, sagebrush intermixes with small shrubby aspen ramets from an old root system, and shrub aspen don't show up on aerial survey photographs, from which counts are made. Aspen can exist in this form for many years, surviving as shrubs or perennial herbs rather than trees, as long as the ramets photosynthesize and stock the roots with carbohydrates.

Success is a human concept that does not take into account aspen's survival strategy tailored for the long term, for existence as a tree or shrub, as a perennial or annual forb. Persistence, not size, is the name of the game.

The glorious undergrowth is one of the charms of an aspen grove. Most aspen communities throughout the West generally have a rich multi-layered understory, a few tall shrubs aproned with lush grasses and interwoven with flowers. Unlike the bare-floored dark conifer forests, sufficient light shafts through the aspen canopy to encourage this abundant herbage that provides excellent wildlife habitat for birds and mammals. Livestock and large wild animals utilize it as much as, if not more than, the adjacent grasslands, for it yields tons of forage and browse per acre annually.

It is the richness of the plant growth that exists under no other major tree community in the West that has made aspen prime grazing territory, a mixed blessing. If allowed to overgraze, cattle trample and destroy plant cover, discourage ground-nesting birds, and reduce the habitat for all the mice and voles that scamper the grove. New ramets are safe from grazing only when they are over five feet tall. Removing more than one-third of the plant cover is an invitation to erosion. Under heavy grazing, the richly varied flora is replaced by one less complex and less palatable, dominated by dandelions and yarrow, black-eyed Susans and coneflowers.

For decades sheepherders trailed their flocks through aspen groves on their way to higher pastures. In the last century sheep heavily grazed the valleys of Idaho's Sawtooth Mountains, following the retreat of snow into higher meadows. Basque sheepherders literally raced for the best areas, trailing the sheep back and forth all summer, camping in the gentle aspen groves until snows drove them down. Some of the lonely messages and erotic pictures carved on aspen, from Steens Mountain in Oregon to the LaSals in Utah, from the Sangre de Cristos in New Mexico to the Carson Mountains in Nevada, document what it was like to trail a band of sheep all summer and have only an aspen grove to talk to.

One of the most lush aspen areas in Colorado graces Kebler Pass west of Crested Butte. In early summer wide-leaved corn lilies and prolific ferns grow waist high in an opulent, thick undergrowth. Concave land surfaces here hold deep soils that remain wet late into the summer, nourishing immense trees and their luxuriant companion plants.

In a small aspen grove in Wyoming, heavenly scents arise from pineapple weed and bedstraw. There are so many flowers I make an inventory by color—of pink there is buckwheat, gilia and geraniums, wild roses and small fireweeds; of blue, harebell and pale larkspur; of lavender, foxglove and daisy; of white, cow parsnip, chickweed and yampa, snowberry and shepherd's purse; of yellow, ragwort, salsify and cinquefoil—a mixture of flowers as lavish as those painted on the border of a medieval manuscript.

Fossil aspen leaves commonly occur in assemblages with many of the plants still associated with aspen: among them bearberry, chokecherry, snowberry, and serviceberry. Today aspen grow in such a wide range of environmental conditions that only four plants can consistently be found in more than half the aspen clones in the intermountain West: snowberry, yarrow, a wheatgrass, and meadowrue. Of these, the delicate, unassuming meadowrue is the only herb found in nearly every western grove.

The same gentler climate within the grove that soothes my spirit fosters this general abundance of accompanying plants—air is more humid, and strong, high-altitude sunlight is gentled. When winds in the canopy blow more than twenty miles per hour, only a breeze tickles my head five feet above the ground. Aspen leaves decompose quickly and enrich the soil with nutrients and organic matter, leaving it better able to hold moisture. Snow lasts longer, and soils beneath aspen groves freeze later and warm earlier. There are many more invertebrates—beetles, snails, ants, fungus gnats, mites—in aspen soils than in conifer soils. The rock on which I perch is so padded, crusted, and scabbed with mosses and lichens that only the sharpest corners poke through; similar rocks outside the grove's shelter are nearly bare, sunstruck and frost riven.

Aspen tolerates a wide variety of soils from talus to clay to volcanic, but grows best on well-drained, deep, loamy soils. But even when habitats are inhospitable, more plants still grow beneath aspen trees than beneath evergreens. Streams of boot-abrading volcanic boulders are common in southernmost Utah. Beneath the scattered aspen there, lacking shrubs and taller herbs, low plants of grasses and sedges, tiny columbine and buckwheats have rooted everywhere there's a patch of blown-in soil, forming one of the simplest aspen understories.

In mid-July in this grove I know so well in Colorado, aspen daisies—fine-petaled lavender flowers with a flat yellow center—ring the grove, lavished with tiny iridescent bees like airborne emeralds. Stiff-stemmed black-eyed Susans, deep pink wild roses and orange hawksbeard brighten the freckled shadows; meadowrue dangles tiny green-earring flowers; pink and white geraniums sound grace-notes, as festive as summer itself. Summer twines around me, an interweaving of color and scent and movement as rich and sprightly and invigorating as a *Brandenburg Concerto*.

Fireweed and aspen, Castle Creek near Aspen, Colorado

Diseased aspen clone, Cathedral Peak region, California

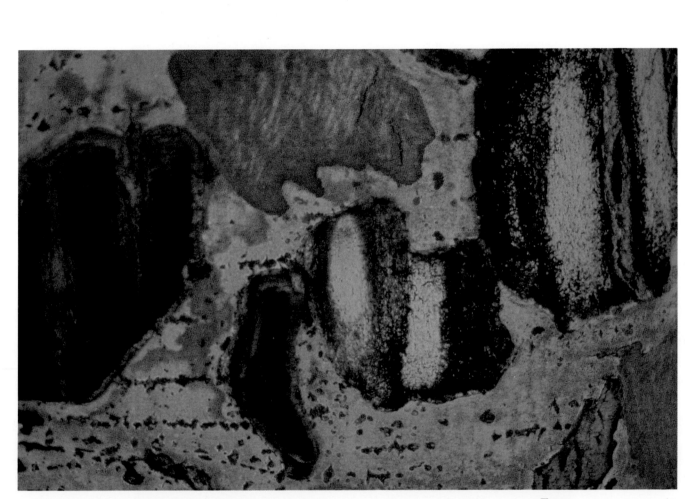

Elk-browsed aspen bole

Rio Santa Barbara Trail, Pecos Wilderness, New Mexico

Waterfall and aspen, White River National Forest, near Vail, Colorado

Young ramets sprouting among horsetails and anemones following beaver cutting

Aspen with wild geranium and yellow parsley, White River National Forest, Colorado

Yellow ragwort and aspen, Grand Mesa, Colorado

Lupine, columbine, and aspen, Grond Mesa, Colorado

Aspen and ferns, Kebler Pass, Colorado

*Basque sheepherder Emmanuel Marcus's
inscription, Toiyabe National Forest, Nevada*

Firestorm-bent trees, Yellowstone National Park, Wyoming

Charred aspen and lupine, one year after Yellowstone fires

Extravagant floral understory, Grand Teton National Park

Circular dot patterns from yellow-bellied sapsucker feeding

Spider-mite gall on aspen leaf

Aspen krummholtz, Niwot Ridge, Colorado

 AUTUMN

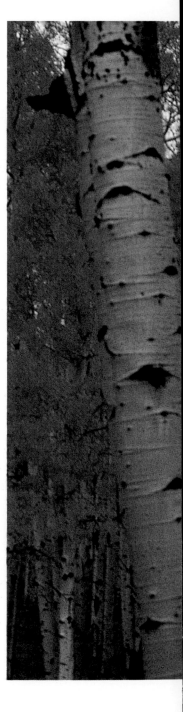

At Constant Friendship this autumn morning my attention is caught by a wind-thrown aspen log which I must have stepped over a hundred times and never noticed. Fans of dirtywhite,leathery fungus shelve out at the base of the bole, evidence of white butt rot, *Fomes applanatus*, a fungus which makes older trees vulnerable to wind-throw. A scrap of its bark lies on the ground, closely pimpled with pale gray bumps centered with black—the fruiting bodies of yet another common fungus, one of the 250 kinds that besiege aspen.

I pull off a large plate of bark and uncover a whole world of small things: empty flat, coiled snail shells, smaller than a thumbtack head, iridescent amber; empty glumes from mountain bromegrass; cow parsnip seeds. Cast-off aspen-bud shells, shiny deep red, are still surplice-wrapped as they were around a leaf whose swelling split them open and shucked them off—such fragile casings that even the lightest breeze lifts them off my palm. They look like molted insect carapaces, delicate and still bearing the shape of the body that inhabited them.

The thin skin of white bark goes early; only a few tattered pieces remain, papery, the white darkened to brown and black. The underside shreds into ribbons and fine threads, dry straw, tatted together with white fungal filaments. I place the fragment back on the log where it lay, untampering with.

Thirty feet farther up are the meandering trails of boring beetles looping through the smooth, satiny wood, as wandering as Diogenes' path while looking for an honest man. Frass, the sawdust and excrement of the boring larvae, still packs some of their trails. Three species of boring beetle attack aspen, each with names only an entomologist could love. Both male and female of *Procryphalus mucronatus* bore narrow tunnels in the outer bark in which eggs are laid; after hatching, the larvae feed on the

Aspen and conifers, Humphrey's Peak region, Arizona

walls of the gallery, pupate over the winter and transform into adults inside the wood, drilling out the following spring.

A *Trypophloeus populi* female follows much the same pattern; the male often plugs the entry with his body to prevent other matings and dies there, a victim of his own fidelity.

In the deepening afternoon, we cross the east flank of Boulder Mountain in Utah, between the towns of Escalante and Torrey. We ascend through aspen thickets, incessant trunks in small, close clones, filigreed with pewter branches. Around nine thousand feet the thickets coalesce into hundreds of acres of aspen, clone after clone, *Populus* populating the world. A lone aspen in the middle of a knoll, cloneless, with no competition for light or water, spreads as amply as an oak.

We come here in search of a grove of giant aspen. We find them standing among boulders of ruddy red and charcoal that stud the bronze-leafed floor of the clone. Younger trees are here but stand apart, distanced from these huge ones whose size and dignity demand space, require deference. They are not flighty Aphrodite trees, dancing and sparkling, given to frivolities. These are the Zeus of the aspen grove.

I can't even get my arms around the boles. Clearly they have well exceeded their life expectancy of two hundred years, although it's often difficult to tell, even from a core, given aspen's inconstancy of growth rings. In unglaciated sections of the country, as here, many clones may have endured many thousands of years. Spared the rigors of Pleistocene ice, they may well be direct descendants of Miocene- and Pliocene-epoch clones going back fifteen million years. The larger, fewer-toothed leaves of Colorado and Utah aspen more closely resemble fossil leaves than those of aspen farther north or in the northeast.

I have no tape measure, so I remove my boot laces, tie them together, and find them not nearly long enough to go round. I settle for bending my notebook around the trunk and marking how many times it goes. One seventy-inch-circumference bole works out to a twenty-two-inch diameter; others have similar girth.

For the first eight feet the trunks are blackened, deeply furrowed and cracked; above, coal-black diamonds and lozenges pattern the bark like giant Tarot cards. Where branches fell they left heavily browed eyes like those of brooding, monster bulls. Monumental and isolated, the giants stand aloof, as if enduring so many winters and so many summers sets them apart, renders them able now to communicate only with others who have seen the same ancient comets, endured the same cruel freezes, withstood the same devastating droughts. They gaze somber-eyed into the distance, the superb survivors, shrouded in dreams.

We head north in late September to the Wasatch Range. Sweeping serpentines and crescents of saffron-yellow aspen scribe the sharply striped tan and blue layers of Mt. Timpanogos. They gild the mountain flank midway down, bracketed by evergreens above and scrub oak below. Clouds stream across the sky, alternately shining and dulling the golden nugget clones. In less than half an hour the cloud puffs coalesce into a single, ominous cloud, sitting on the top of Mt. Timpanogos like a bad omen, fading the aspen to murky amber.

Farther up the mountain every bole quirks, curves, or spirals, never having decided which way was up. Wind torments and twists every leaf blade, but the leaves hold fast. The leaves are so numerous and so small that the effect is like wind blowing a shower of light sparks across a pond. The leaves hang in solid groups until the wind interrupts the order and sets them swinging, fragments the clumps, reforms the tree. Suddenly a thousand leaves explode out of the trees, and all land on the ground, stems up, dull side down.

The next clone is a uniformity of ten-inch-diameter boles as regular as a picket fence. Their leaves pave the hillside like Byzantine gold tesserae laid in a pavement so that ground and treetop are one color, gold connected to gold by ivory staves, a chryselephantine screen.

Far south, in the Chiricahua Mountains of Arizona, a west-facing ridge falls sharply away below, stair-stepped with aspen. Looking down on the crowns, their luminosity is extraordinary in the late afternoon light that pulses through the leaves in a throbbing cadmium yellow.

Northeasterners may praise their massive maples and grandiose oaks, all those russets and reds, but none of those leaves ignite light as aspen do. No one has ever penned an essay on aspen, no one ever composed an aspen string quartet or an aspen rhapsody, nobody ever sprinkled aspen seeds across the country. But a sonnet in their praise is being written, even as I watch, by a breeze and a slant of October sunshine, floating into twilight.

Ten of five on an autumn evening, Constant Friendship. The sky floats gray feathers on the far ridge, and an end-of-the-day rain plays gentle arpeggios on my rain jacket. I crest a hillside somber with spruce, serious trees humorless as winter. The wind swims through their branches and they respond with lugubrious sighings, not the sibilant, tissue-paper whispers of aspen.

From this height the crowns of the aspen in the valley below thread it with tawny topaz traceries. These leaves a quick week ago were a rich, raffish yellow, distilled sunshine pressed and concentrated into a small leaf, multiplied by a million to a glory. In this chilling evening I know that this is the sad yellow which Persephone saw with dread. Spring seems to come so slowly, autumn so fast, I wonder if it is my eagerness for sun warmth to heat my bones that makes spring such a laggard, and my reluctance to feel the marrow cooling that makes fall's advance so unwelcome and precipitous.

With leaf fall the aspen become transitory, ephemeral, yet some-how more lasting, more locked into memory than the stolid conifers that hold sway all year long. From this vantage I see the aspen from a different perspective, see the beauty of their bark as their survival and their vulnerability, see them as trees fragile and incredibly tough, see them as ethereal but persisting across the epochs, see them for their dichotomies and their simplicities, their Phoenix-like need for fire and destruction to raise them out of the ashes of their own decay. Yet this evening all the crosscurrents dissolve in the exquisite serenity of the aspen themselves.

The evening wind frets everything, especially those snippets of leaf and bark attached at one end, leaving the other free to fidget, twitch, quiver, each at its own tempo. The wind, self-important, officious, has no patience with leaves and scythes through them, sending them in giddy whirls through the grove.

Despite the wind, there is a peacefulness here, a time for going down just as there is a time for budding out, a sense of flow. It is not the yearly cycle that speaks, but the cycle of centuries, of millennia, of trees passing on and trees beginning anew, a larger rhythm from which the tyranny of a life span dissolves into a quietness of gold and gray.

Almost six. Rain drifts in, softens the contours, the colors, the shapes into a multi-layered, subtle collage of torn tissue, overlaid, blurred, interblended. To the west, bands of clear sky brighten the horizon: lavender and apricot and pearl, overhung with shreds of clouds through which a last shaft of sunlight warms the trees below.

In this dimming dayness, this twilight of skytime, the aspen remain poignantly bright, glowing with light while the rest of the world goes down. Despite being damp, despite being tired, I am inexplicably content. Perhaps it is that I am no longer afraid of winter.

La Veta Pass, Colorado

Fish Lake National Forest, Utah

Sangre de Cristo Mountains, Colorado

Chiricahua Mountains, Arizona

Mount Timpanogos, Utah

Red aspen below Mount McKinnon, Utah

Pikes Peak, Colorado

Boulder Mountain, Utah

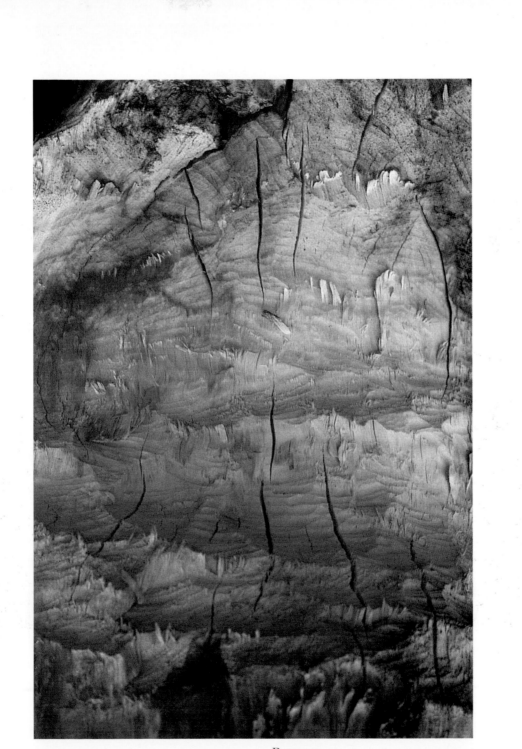

Bole damage from beaver scraping

Pikes Peak region, Colorado

San Juan Mountains, Colorado

Clonal variations

La Sal Mountains, Utah

Hoosier Pass, Colorado

Aspen near Telluride, Colorado

Apache-Sitgreaves National Forest, Arizona